Usborne

# The Bug
# who wanted
# a Hug

Russell Punter

Illustrated by Siân Roberts

This story's full of insects –

earwigs,

wasps

and slugs.

Plus Moth,

Bee,

ants,

some fireflies...

and a beetle in
need of a hug.

Meet Bob the water beetle.

His home is warm and snug.

But poor Bob has no friends
and so...

he never gets a hug.

"I need to meet some bugs," he thinks.

"I'm lonely and I'm glum."

So Bob decides to find some pals.

He comes across
a football match.

The game's well
under way.

"I'll make friends with these teams," thinks Bob.

He stops to watch them play.

Just then, an earwig
scores a goal.

His team mates
shout and cheer.

"Can *I* join in your game?" Bob asks.

"Okay," the earwigs say.

The ball soon
comes Bob's way.

Bob kicks the ball
towards the goal.

The ball flies wide.

He makes a mess of
every shot.

# The final score is 14-1.

There's no chance of
a hug for Bob.

"I'll try my luck elsewhere," thinks Bob.

A line of bugs goes by.

They're off to play some keep fit games.

Bob spots a course
of obstacles.

A race is due to start.

Bob quickly joins the yellow team.

Bob springs nimbly

through
the rings,

along the log...

But when he slides inside
the tube...

he finds that he is stuck!

"Get a move on!"
cry the flies.

"We're losing!"
shout the slugs.

The red team cross the finish line...

and give each other hugs.

At last, Bob pops out
from the tube.

The yellow team all look fed up.

Bob trudges on his way.

Bob sees a sign
outside a hall.

Dance contest
- here today.

Inside, the dance floor's packed with bugs.

The couples swing and sway.

Who's won the prize
for finest jive?

Step forward,
Moth and Slug!

The judge holds out
a silver cup...

and Moth gives
Slug a hug.

The disco contest's coming next.

Bob asks a bee to dance.

Bob thinks they stand
a chance.

But Bob has never danced before. He tries to strut his stuff...

"A dance disaster!"
cries the judge.

Bee flies off in a huff.

Now Bob the beetle's feeling low.

He limps down to the
river bank.

He's one unhappy bug.

An ant sits on the water's edge.

"It's just not fair," she sighs.

She looks fed up.
Bob asks her why.

"I can't swim," she replies.

40

"I'll teach you how to swim," says Bob.

"It's easy. Just watch me."

So Bob spends *all* day
with the ant.

She learns so much
from him.

Just as the sun's about to set, the ant cries...

The ant gives Bob
a great big hug.

She almost dents
his shell.

But wait, the hugs
aren't over yet.

Ant's friends join in
as well.

"What a teacher!"
comes the cheer.

He's loved by all the bugs.

Now Bob's new life is full of friends...

Bob Beetle's swimming lessons here!

and snuggly wuggly hugs.

Designed by Jodie Smith
Series editor: Lesley Sims

Reading consultant: Alison Kelly

First published in 2022 by Usborne Publishing Ltd.,
83-85 Saffron Hill, London EC1N 8RT, England. usborne.com
Copyright © 2022 Usborne Publishing Ltd.

All rights reserved. No part of this publication may be reproduced, stored
in a retrieval system or transmitted in any form or by any means without
the prior permission of the publisher. The name Usborne and the Balloon logo
are Trade Marks of Usborne Publishing Ltd.